G000276047

The Little Book of
Dougal™

First published 2005 by Boxtree
an imprint of Pan Macmillan Ltd
Pan Macmillan, 20 New Wharf Road, London N1 9RR
Basingstoke and Oxford
Associated companies throughout the world
www.panmacmillan.com

ISBN 0 7522 1570 1

Produced under license by Pathe Pictures Limited and Magic Rights Limited

Pathé Pictures presents in association with the UK Film Council and Pathé Renn, Pricel, France 2 Cinema and
Canal + a Films Action / SPZ Entertainment/ bolexbrothers Production
THE MAGIC ROUNDABOUT
Tom Baker Jim Broadbent Joanna Lumley Ian McKellen Kylie Minogue Bill Nighy Robbie Williams Ray Winstone
Associate Producers Claude Gorsky Linda Marks Bruce Higham Andy Leighton Vertigo Productions
Based upon original characters created by Serge Danot with the participation of Martine Danot
Co Writers Raoff Sanoussi Stéphane Sanoussi
Screenplay by Paul Bassett Davies with additional material by Tad Safran
Executive Producers Francois Ivernel Cameron McCracken Jill Sinclair Jake Eberts
Producers Laurent Rodon Pascal Rodon
Directed By Jean Duval Frank Passingham Dave Borthwick
© Pathé Fund Limited 2004.

1 3 5 7 9 8 6 4 2

A CIP catalogue record for this book is available from the British Library.

Designed by seagulls

Printed by Proost, Belgium

The Little Book of
Dougal™

B⊞XTREE

'Have you seen our friend Dougal? - big black nose, looks like a bad hair day on legs?'

'I thought dogs were supposed to fetch.'

'My forte has always been "sit Dougal". That, and "stay, Dougal, stay".'

'I was a very happy
puppy. My first
memories are of
catching tennis
balls with Florence.'

'Look sweets
for my sweet
Dougal.'

'I think I'll take
care of those
lollipops first!'

'It starts with some sweets, maybe an iced bun, and before you know it you're on two bags of sugar a day. Maybe you've got a problem, my furry friend.'

'What's for dinner anyway, I'm famished.'

'It's lucky I brought
some secret supplies.
Mmmmmm...'

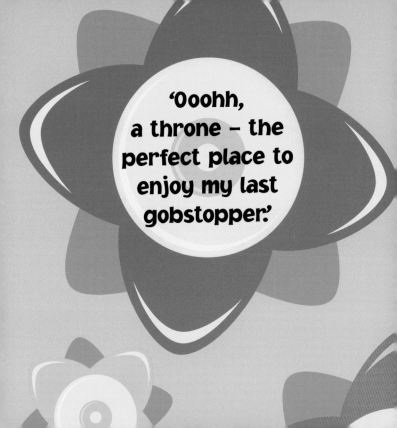

'You can eat
as much as
you like!'

'I only wanted
to get my teeth
into some sweeties.'

'Why do I have to be the guard dog? What's wrong with a guard snail or guard cow?'

'Now, you dim-
witted draft
excluder, tell
me everything.'

'You've eaten
twenty-seven
sugar-cubes!'

'It's what any
incredibly heroic
dog would do.'

'I'll not rest until
I've done everything
in my power to bake
things right!'

'Just in time for lunch.'

'I've learnt my lesson.
I'm not having anything
more to do with lollipops.
Or gobstoppers.
Or toffees...'

'I've learnt my lesson.
I'm not having anything
more to do with lollipops.
Or gobstoppers.
Or toffees...'